AF147301

Coastal Processes and Landforms

- Read, engage and learn!
- Full colour, illustrated Topic Booklet.
- Glossary, Memory Map, Active Learning Game & Flashcards.
- Ideal for ISEB 13+ Common Entrance and KS3 pupils.

Endorsed by:

ISEB Independent Schools Examinations Board

This Oaka™ Books Topic Booklet goes hand in hand with the Active Learning Pack on this topic. The pack includes a Write Your Own Notes Booklet, an Active Learning Game and Question & Answer Flashcards.

Fresh Focus on Learning

Oaka™ BOOKS

Coastal Processes and Landform Glossary

 **Abrasion:** Waves throw sand and pebbles against the cliff. This causes erosion to the cliff base.

 **Constructive Waves:** Waves that deposit eroded material and build up the beach.

 **Attrition:** Waves smash pebbles and rocks into each other. This breaks them up.

 **Corrosion:** Weak acid in the sea water dissolves some rocks. The dissolved rock is carried away in solution.

 **Backwash:** The water that runs **back** into the sea after a wave has broken.

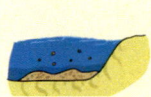 **Deposition:** The dropping of eroded material. Happens when water flows slowly or is shallow.

 **Bar:** A thin strip of sand and shingle that spreads across a bay.

 **Destructive Waves:** Big waves that erode the beach. Great for surfing!

 **Bay:** An area of soft rock that has been eroded.

 **Erosion:** The breaking down and carrying away of rocks.

 **Beach Nourishment:** Building up the beach using natural materials.

 **Fetch:** The distance a wave has travelled.

 **Coastal Zone:** The thin strip between land and sea.

 **Groynes:** Rigid structures that stop a beach being eroded away by longshore drift.

 **Conflict:** When different groups of people want different things.

 **Hard Engineering:** Structures built to protect the coastline.

Coastal Processes and Landform Glossary

 **Headland:** An area of hard rock that erodes more slowly than softer rock around it.

 **Soft Engineering:** Work to protect the coastal zone using natural materials.

 **Hydraulic Action:** The force of water or air when it is trapped in joints and cracks in rock.

 **Spit:** Long, thin stretches of beach material found across a river mouth or where the coast changes direction.

 **Longshore Drift:** The movement (transport) of eroded material along the coast.

 **Swash:** The water that runs **up** the beach when a wave breaks.

 **Managed Retreat:** Adding more sand or shingle to widen the beach.

 **Tombolo:** A spit that connects an island to the mainland.

 **Rip Rap:** Large rocks placed on the coast to absorb the power of the waves.

 **Transportation:** The movement of eroded material along the coast.

 **Salt Marshes:** Coastal marsh formed behind a spit.

 **Weathering:** The wearing away of rocks (note: this is different from erosion).

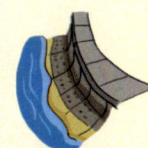 **Sea Wall:** Helps protect the area behind it from flooding.

 **Stewardship:** Looking after the environment and resources for future generations.

Coastal Erosion

1 Coasts and the Coastal Zone

Coasts are shaped by the sea and by **wave action.**

- The coast is where land meets the sea.

- The **coastal zone** is a thin strip between land and sea.

- This strip is being changed by **erosion** and **weathering** all the time.

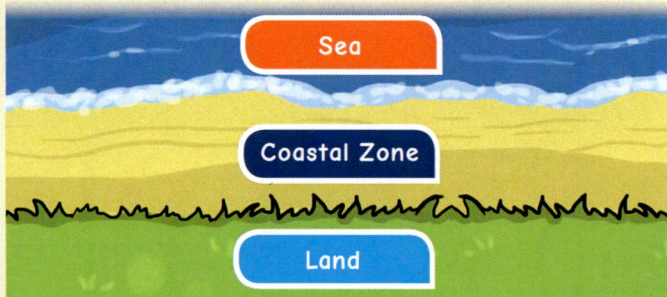

Sea

Coastal Zone

Land

2 Types of Coastal Area Include...

- beaches, (pebbles/rock/sand)
- sand dunes
- salt marshes
- cliffs
- natural harbours
- seaside resorts

3 Key Processes

The UK has about **17,820 km** of coastline!

3 key processes affect the coast:

- **erosion**: the 'wearing away' of material

- **transportation**: the movement of material up, down and along the coast

- **deposition**: the dropping of eroded material.

Factors Affecting Coastal Erosion

4   Rock Type

- Hard rock, like limestone, forms **steep cliffs.**
- **Soft** rock, like clay, forms **bays.**

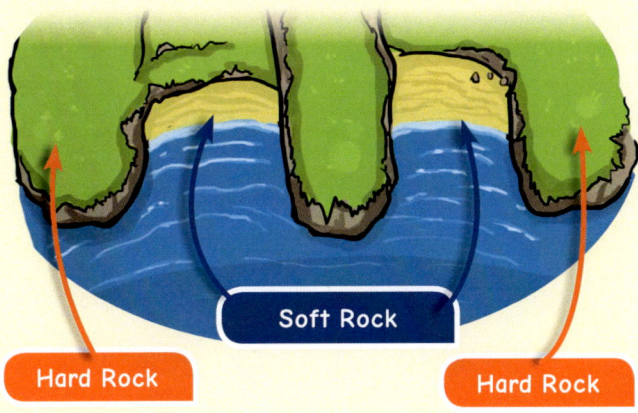

Soft Rock

Hard Rock

Hard Rock

5   Rock Structure

- Where the rocks are at **an angle** to the **coast**, they will **erode** at **different rates.**

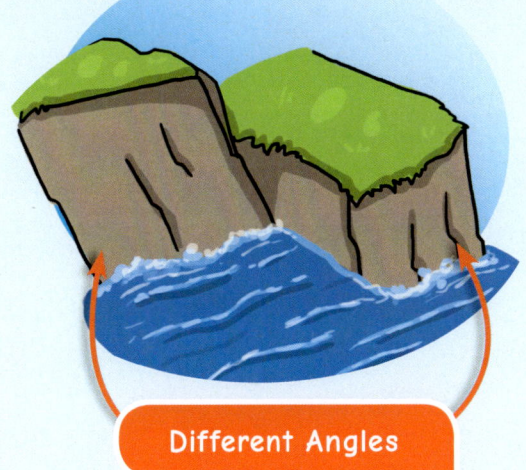

Different Angles

6   Shape of the coast

- **Headlands** are exposed.
- **Bays** are sheltered so they **erode** more slowly.
- Bays often include some deposition forming a beach.

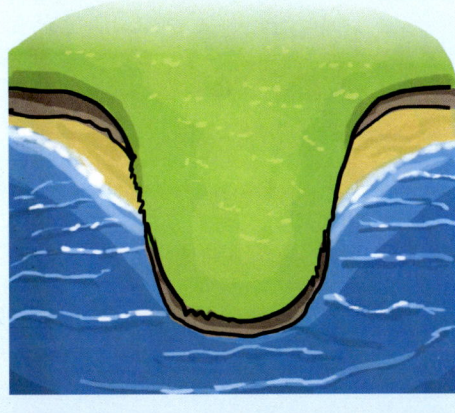

7   Waves

- Waves have a huge impact on the coastal zone.
- They are created by **wind** blowing over the sea.

Wave Power

8   Friction on Water

- The friction of the wind on the sea's surface creates **swell.**
- This friction makes water particles **rotate** and the wave moves forward.

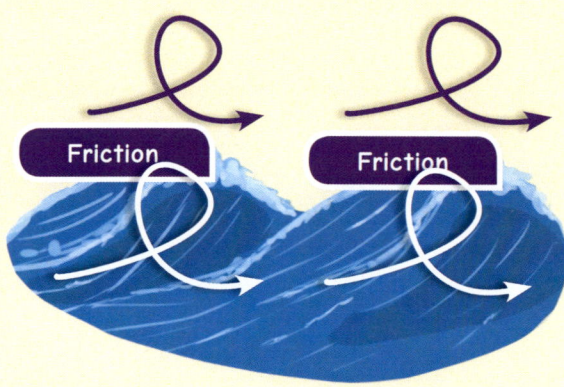

9   Wave Size and Energy

- Is affected by the strength of the wind.
- How long it has been blowing.
- How far the wave has travelled **(fetch).**

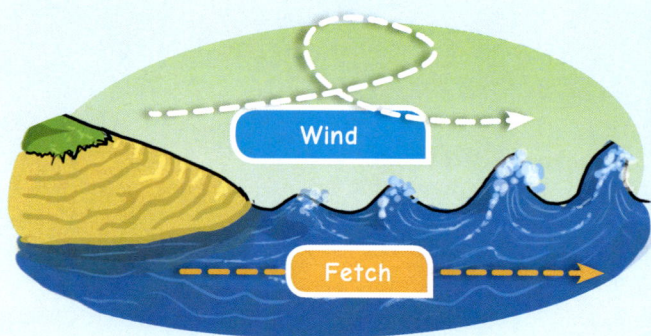

10   How Waves Work

- When a wave breaks, water is washed **up** the beach.
- This is called the **swash.**

- The wave then moves **back down** the beach.
- This is called the **backwash.**

11   Waves Can Be...

Destructive:
- these **erode.**

Constructive:
- these **deposit** and **build.**

Wave Power

12   Destructive Waves

- are usually **big** (great for surfers!)

- have a long **fetch**

- have strong **backwash**

- have weak **swash**

- are **high and steep**

- **they erode.**

Weak Swash

Strong Backwash

13   Constructive Waves

- are **less** powerful

- form in **calmer** weather

- have a strong **swash**

- and a weak **backwash**

- are **lower** in height

- **deposit** material.

Strong Swash

Deposited Material

Weak Backwash

Coastal Erosion

14   Coastal Erosion

- The wearing away and breaking of rock along coasts.

15   Destructive Waves

Destructive waves erode by:

- **Hydraulic action**

- **Abrasion**

- **Attrition**

- **Corrosion (and Solution)**

16   Hydraulic Action

- Water or air can be trapped in joints and cracks in a cliff.
- A wave breaks and **compresses** this air.
- The cliff is **weakened** and **erodes**.
- A cave is formed.

Cliff erodes

- Seawater compresses the trapped air in the cave.
- This blasts away at the inside of the cave.
- A blow hole may be formed.

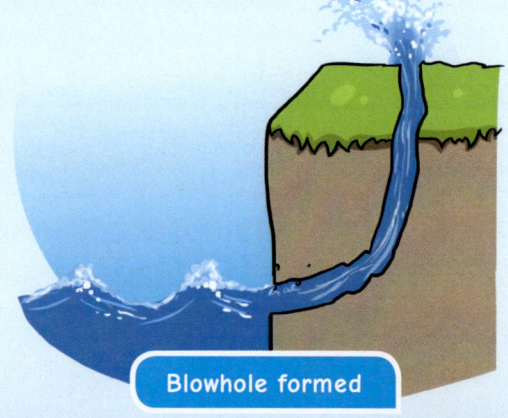

Blowhole formed

Coastal Erosion

17 Abrasion

- Waves throw sand and pebbles against the cliff.

- This causes damage and **erosion**. In **storms**, **big rocks** cause **more damage**.

Sand and pebbles crash against rocks

18 Attrition

- Waves smash pebbles and rocks into each other.

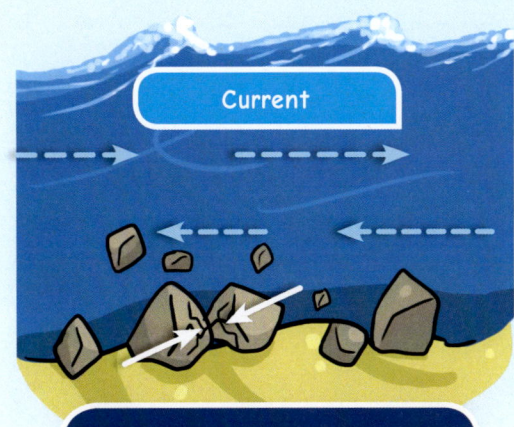

Current

Pebbles and rocks smash together

19 Further Attrition

- The rocks and pebbles break and become smoother.

Current

Breaking up into smoother pieces

20 Corrosion

- Weak acid in sea water dissolves some rocks (e.g. **limestone** and **chalk**).

- These are carried away in **solution**.

Cliff erodes

Weak acid in sea water

Features formed by Erosion

21   Cliffs

Weather **weakens** the top of the cliff.

The **sea** cuts into the bottom of the cliff (**notch**).

The cliff **collapses** and **retreats**

22   Headlands and Bays

- **Soft rocks**, like **clay** and **sand**, erode faster than **hard** rocks, like **chalk**.

- Where rock is in bands of soft/hard/soft, the **hard** rock sticks out as a **headland**.

- The soft rock erodes, forming bays.

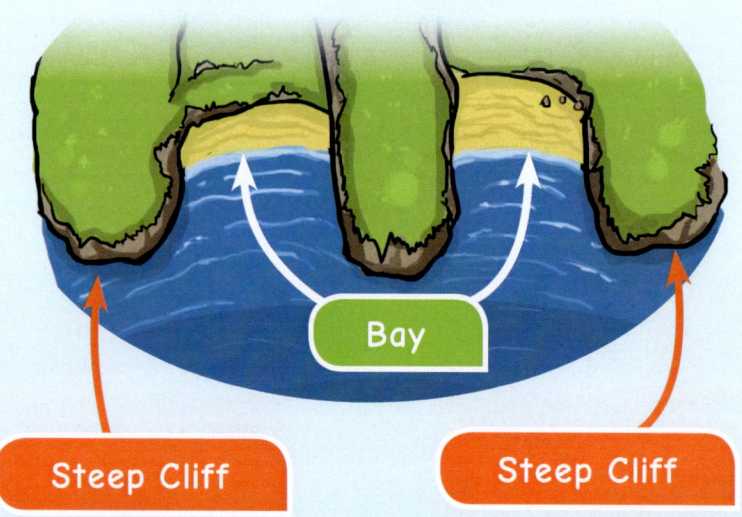

Bay

Steep Cliff   Steep Cliff

Features formed by Erosion

23 Cave

- **Caves** form when waves are pushed into a crack in the rock

- **The** hydraulic action **wears** away the rock until a **cave** is made.

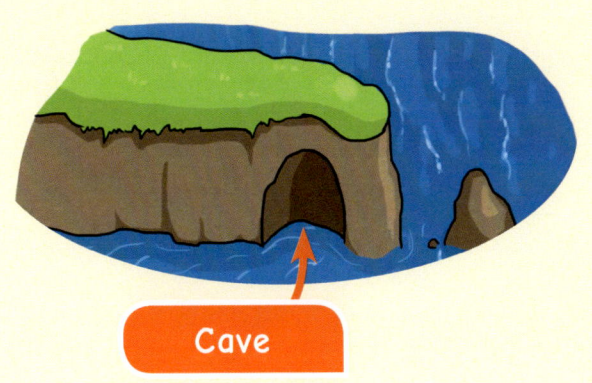

Cave

24 Arch

- If the **cave** is in a **headland**, it can wear right through the rock to form an **arch**.

Cave wears through rock

25 Stack

- The **arch** becomes too big to support the top.

- The top **collapses**.

- This leaves a **stack**, which is **separate** from the **headland**.

- The **stack** is weathered and eroded.

- It gets smaller and then becomes a **pinnacle**.

- Over time, the **stump** will disappear.

Pinnacle

Stump

Collapses

Leaves a stack

Coastal Deposition

26 Formation of Beaches

- Beaches are formed by **deposition**.

- This is the **dropping** of **eroded material** by the water.

Deposited material

27 Deposition

Deposition will happen when...

- **waves** enter shallow water or
- **waves** enter a sheltered bay or
- it is **calm**, with little **wind.**

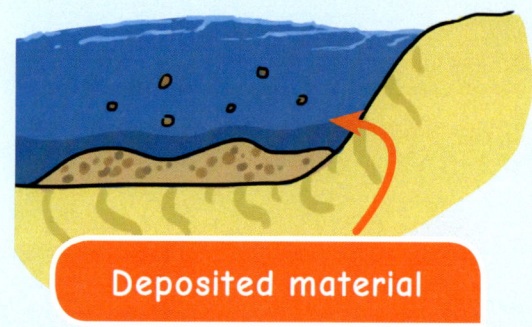

Deposited material

28 Longshore Drift

- Longshore Drift moves **eroded material along** the coast.

- It can **change** the **shape** of the **beach** every day!

29 How Longshore Drift Works

- **Waves** approach the coast at an **angle**.

- **Swash** carries material up the beach at an **angle**.

Swash carries material up the beach

Beaches

30 Zig Zag Movement

- **Backwash** carries **material back** at a **right angle**.
- The **zig-zag** carries material along.

31 Beaches

- Beaches are formed by **deposition**. **Constructive** waves help build beaches.
- **Material** on a **beach varies in size** as you **move away** from the **shoreline**.

Size varies further away from the shoreline

32 Shape of Beaches

- The **shape** of the **beach** is called the **profile**.
- **Sandy** beaches slope **gently**.

Gentle Slope

33 Shingle and Pebbles

- **Shingle** and **pebble beaches** are **steeper**.

Steep Slope

Features of Beaches

34   Spit

- **Spits** are caused by **deposition**.

- They are **long, thin stretches** of **beach material**.

- They can be found **across a river mouth** or **where the coast changes direction**.

- **Joined** to the land at one end.

- Caused by **longshore drift**.

- Follow the **direction** of the **prevailing** wind.

- Behind a spit water slows down.

- Deposition here may form a salt marsh.

Salt Marsh

35   Bar

- A thin ridge of sand and shingle spreads across a bay.

- Formed by **longshore drift**.

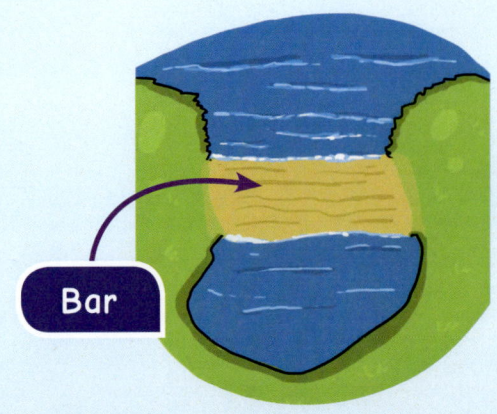

Bar

36   Tombolo

- Is a **spit** connecting an **island** to the **mainland**.

An example is **Chesil Beach**.

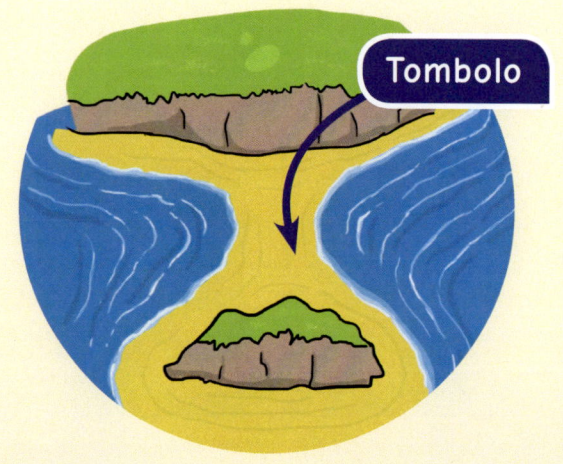

Tombolo

The Importance of Coasts

37 — Salt Marshes & Mudflats

Form behind spits where there is:

- **more shelter**
- less water **movement**
- **more deposition.**
- They are important wildlife habitats.

38 — Living and Working

Coasts are important for lots of reasons and lots of people:

- Places to **live.**

- Coastal river estuaries are important for heavy industry and container ports.

39 — Tourism

- Places to **relax**, (holidays and tourism.
- Beautiful scenery.

40 — Habitats

- Wildlife habitats

- Education

This booklet is not to be photocopied. Thank you.

12

Coastal Flood Protection

41   Coastal Management

There are 2 main types of management:

- Hard engineering.

- Soft engineering.

42   Hard Engineering

Involves building structures to protect the coast.

Structures such as...

- A Sea Wall.

- Groynes

- Rip Rap

43   Sea Walls

+ **Protect** the **land/cliffs** behind it.

+ Prevent **floods**.

- Very **expensive**.

- Can look **ugly**.

- Waves **bounce off** and move material from the beach.

44   Groynes

+ Help **stop longshore drift** moving material.

+ Can **help build beaches**.

- Create problems by starving other beaches.

- Can be **ugly**.

Coastal Flood Protection

45   Rip Rap

+ Large rocks **absorb** the **power** of the **waves**.

- If the **waves** are **very strong** the **rocks** can **move**.

- Can look **ugly**.

46   Soft Engineering

• Works with **nature** or uses **natural materials**.

• Extends the **width** of the beach.

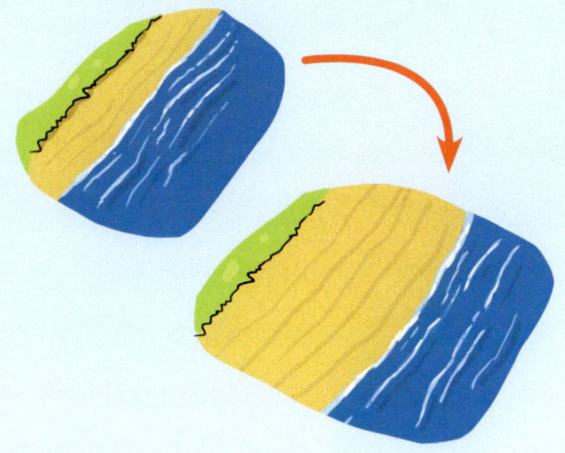

47   Beach Nourishment

+ **Adds material** to the **beach**.
+ Is **natural** and quite **cheap**.

- Does not last long.

48   Managed Retreat

Land becomes marsh.

+ Creates **new habitats**.
+ Is **natural**.

- **Land** is **lost**.

Managing Conflict

49 Conflicts In Managing Coasts

- **Different groups** want different things.

Save our houses!!

Save our wildlife!!

Save our farmland!!

Help our business!!

50 Groups With An Interest

Groups with an interest include:

- people who live by the coast
- people who work there
- developers.
- industry

51 Groups With An Interest

- **Councils**

  Need Housing

- **Tourist boards**

  Need to attract visitors

- **National parks**

  Need to protect the countryside

- **Industry**

  Needs transport routes

52 Why Is There Conflict?

- A person who **lives** by the coast may want to be **protected** from **flooding**.

- **Tourist boards** may not want **ugly engineering**.

Visit our Beaches

This booklet is not to be photocopied. Thank you.

Managing Conflict

53 Conflict

- **Developers** may want to **protect land** they want to **build on**.

- **Environmentalists** don't want the **habitat spoiled**.

Don't spoil the habitat!!

54 Conflict

- **National parks** may want **managed retreat**.

- **Farmers** will not want to **lose land**.

55 Conflict

- Coasts need **protecting but** people need to talk to get the **best result** for everyone.

- **Stewardship** is **looking after the environment and resources for future generations**.

- We are all responsible for protecting our coasts.

Meeting to discuss how to work together.

About Oaka Books

Children learn best when they are engaged...

Our aim is to help children enjoy learning by making it fun! That way they will succeed.

This topic pack follows the Common Entrance syllabus and National Curriculum guidelines for ISEB 13+ KS3.

The design and layout of our books follow guidelines from the British Dyslexia Association.

ISBN 978-1-909892-43-9
9 781909 892439

CE/KS3 Ge-
Coastal Erosion

Topic Booklet

Three Easy Steps

Read: the easy to follow bullet point Topic Booklet.

Engage: Play the Active Learning Game.

Learn: When you understand the topic, test yourself using the Write Your Own Notes Book. You can use the Topic Booklet to help if you get stuck.

One (short) Topic at a time:

For some students, a big book is a big turn off. That's why we focus on one topic at a time. Short and to the point.

Reading Age

This booklet is suitable for children with a reading age of 10 ½ years.

Topic Packs for KS1, KS2 & KS3 Include:

History
Geography
Chemistry
Biology
Physics
French
Maths

Please visit www.oakabooks.co.uk for more information about forthcoming titles

© Copyright 2016 Oaka Books. All rights reserved.
Written by Kate Doehren, MA Ed, B.Ed Hons, RSA Dip, Sp LD/Dyslexia. Director of Learning Support, Hurstpierpoint College. Edited by Simon Lewis, ISEB Geography Editor & Setting Team Leader. Illustrations by Laurence Andrew Page.

First paperback edition printed 2014 in the United Kingdom.
A catalogue record for this book is available from the British Library.

ISBN 978-1-909892-43-9
No part of this book shall be reproduced or transmitted in any form or by any means, electronic or mechanical, including photocopying, recording or by any information retrieval system without written permission of the copyright owner or a licence permitting restricted copying issued by the Copyright Licensing Agency Ltd, Saffron House, 6-10 Kirby Street, London EC1N 8TS Tel: 020 7400 3100   Fax: 020 7400 3101   Email: cla@cla.co.uk   Web: www.cla.co.uk

Designed, set and published by Oaka™ Books.
To order other titles from Oaka™ Books, please email info@oakabooks.co.uk or visit www.oakabooks.co.uk, or phone: +44 (023) 92 388519.

Acknowledgements
Our huge thanks go to the many teachers who have been involved in the development of this series of learning guides. Special thanks to Joy Gardiner, for producing hundreds of illustrations, to Kate Doehren, for her enthusiasm and invaluable assistance to my wonderful daughter Sophie, for being the inspiration for the books and, of course, to Charlie, for believing in them.

ISBN 978-1-909892-43-9   Produced in association with Kate Doehren, MA Ed, B.Ed Hons, RSA Dip, Sp LD/Dyslexia
Director of Learning Support, Hurstpierpoint College
© Copyright Oaka™ Books 2016